Based on the best-selling keyboard method *by Kenneth Baker.*

THE COMPLETE KEYBOARD PLAYER

New Chart Hits

Wise Publications
part of The Music Sales Group
London/New York/Paris/Sydney/Copenhagen/Berlin/Madrid/Tokyo

Published by
Wise Publications
14-15 Berners Street, London W1T 3LJ, UK.

Exclusive Distributors:
Music Sales Limited
Distribution Centre, Newmarket Road, Bury St Edmunds, Suffolk IP33 3YB, UK.
Music Sales Pty Limited
120 Rothschild Avenue, Rosebery, NSW 2018, Australia.

This book © Copyright 2006 Wise Publications,
a division of Music Sales Limited.
Order No. AM988053
ISBN 1-84609-808-4

Music arranged by Paul Honey.
Music processed by Paul Ewers Music Design.
Edited by Rachel Payne.
Cover photograph courtesy of Michael Caulfield/wireimage.com
Printed in the EU.

Your Guarantee of Quality
As publishers, we strive to produce every book
to the highest commercial standards.
This book has been carefully designed to minimise awkward
page turns and to make playing from it a real pleasure.
Particular care has been given to specifying acid-free, neutral-sized paper
made from pulps which have not been elemental chlorine bleached.
This pulp is from farmed sustainable forests and was produced with special
regard for the environment. Throughout, the printing and binding have been
planned to ensure a sturdy, attractive publication which should give years of enjoyment.
If your copy fails to meet our high standards, please inform us and
we will gladly replace it.

www.musicsales.com

Master Chord Chart

C
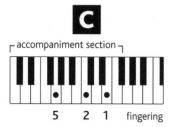

accompaniment section

5   2   1   fingering

Cm
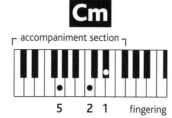

accompaniment section

5   2   1   fingering

C 7
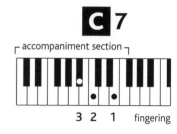

accompaniment section

3   2   1   fingering

D♭(C♯)
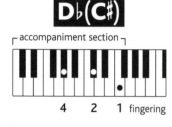

accompaniment section

4   2   1   fingering

D♭(C♯)m

accompaniment section

4   2   1   fingering

D♭(C♯) 7
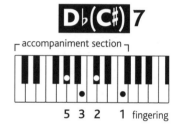

accompaniment section

5   3   2   1   fingering

D
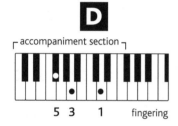

accompaniment section

5   3   1   fingering

Dm
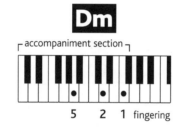

accompaniment section

5   2   1   fingering

D 7
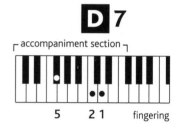

accompaniment section

5   2 1   fingering

E♭(D♯)
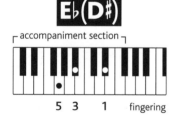

accompaniment section

5   3   1   fingering

E♭(D♯)m
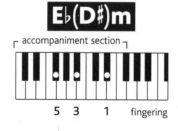

accompaniment section

5   3   1   fingering

E♭(D♯) 7
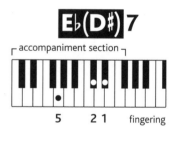

accompaniment section

5   2 1   fingering

E
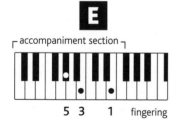

accompaniment section

5   3   1   fingering

Em
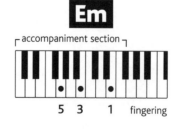

accompaniment section

5   3   1   fingering

E 7
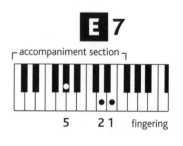

accompaniment section

5   2 1   fingering

F
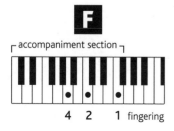

accompaniment section

4   2   1   fingering

Fm
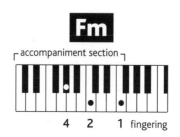

accompaniment section

4   2   1   fingering

F 7
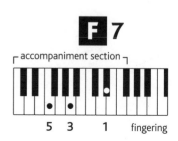

accompaniment section

5   3   1   fingering

Master Chord Chart

G♭(F♯)
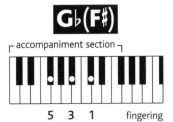
accompaniment section
5 3 1 fingering

G♭(F♯)m
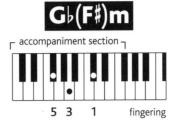
accompaniment section
5 3 1 fingering

G♭(F♯)7
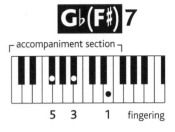
accompaniment section
5 3 1 fingering

G
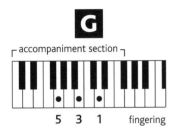
accompaniment section
5 3 1 fingering

Gm
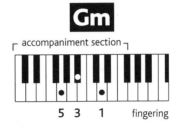
accompaniment section
5 3 1 fingering

G7
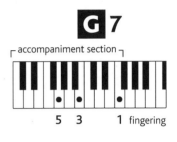
accompaniment section
5 3 1 fingering

A♭(G♯)
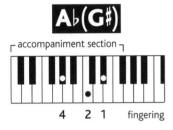
accompaniment section
4 2 1 fingering

A♭(G♯)m
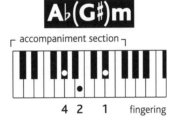
accompaniment section
4 2 1 fingering

A♭(G♯)7
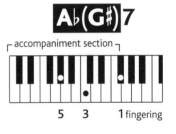
accompaniment section
5 3 1 fingering

A
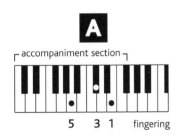
accompaniment section
5 3 1 fingering

Am
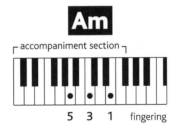
accompaniment section
5 3 1 fingering

A7
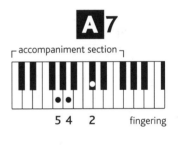
accompaniment section
5 4 2 fingering

B♭
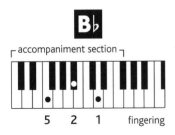
accompaniment section
5 2 1 fingering

B♭m
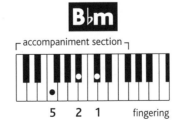
accompaniment section
5 2 1 fingering

B♭7
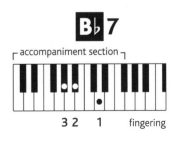
accompaniment section
3 2 1 fingering

B
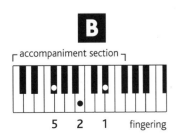
accompaniment section
5 2 1 fingering

Bm
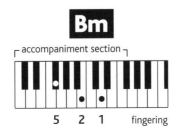
accompaniment section
5 2 1 fingering

B7
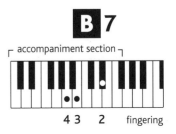
accompaniment section
4 3 2 fingering

Because Of You

Words & Music by Kelly Clarkson, Ben Moody & David Hodges

Voice: **Clarinet**
Rhythm: **8th beat Pop**
Tempo: ♩ = 70

I will not make the same mis-takes that you did; I___ will_ not let my-self

'cause my heart so much mi-se-ry. I will not break___ the

way you did; you fell so hard. I've learned the hard way to

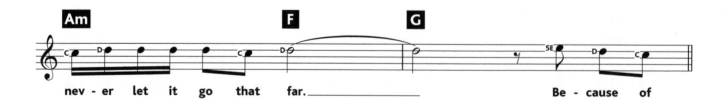

nev-er let it go that far.___ Be - cause of

you, I nev-er stray too far from the side - walk. Be - cause of

you, I learned to play on the safe side so I don't get hurt. Be - cause of

you, I find it hard to trust not on - ly me but ev -'ry one a - round me. Be - cause of

new hand position

you,_____ I am a - fraid. I watched you

die, I heard you cry ev -'ry night in your sleep.__ I was so

young, you should have known bet - ter than to lean on me. You nev - er

thought of an - y - one else, you just saw your pain;__ and now I

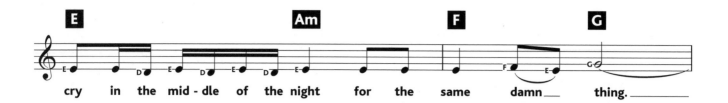

cry in the mid-dle of the night for the same damn___ thing.___

new hand position

___ Be - cause of you, I nev - er stray too far from the

side - walk. Be - cause of you, I learned to play on the safe side so I

don't get hurt. Be - cause of you, I find it hard to trust not on - ly

me but ev - 'ry one a - round me. Be - cause of you,___ I am a -

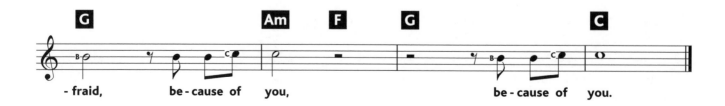

- fraid, be - cause of you, be - cause of you.

Check On It

Words by Beyonce Knowles, Kelendria Rowland, Kasseem Dean, Sean Garrett & Mich Williams
Music by Beyonce Knowles, Kelendria Rowland, Kasseem Dean & Sean Garrett

Voice: **Marimba or vibes**
Rhythm: **8th beat**
Tempo: ♩ = 152

Ooh, boy, you look - ing like you like what you see. Won't you

come ov - er and check up on it? I'm - a let you work up on it.

La - dies, let him check up on it watch it while he check up on it.

Dip it, pop it, twirl it, stop it; check on me. If you

got it, flaunt it! Boy, I know you want it.

While I turn a - round you, watch me check up on. You know you

watch - ing me shake it, I see it on your face. You can't

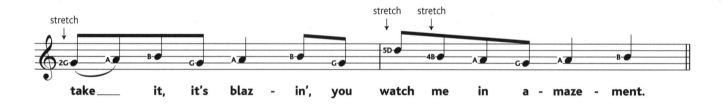

take___ it, it's blaz - in', you watch me in a - maze - ment.

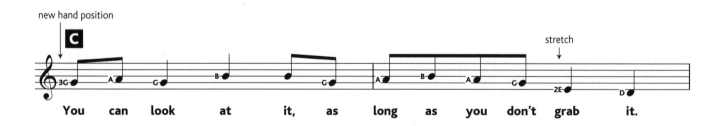

You can look at it, as long as you don't grab it.

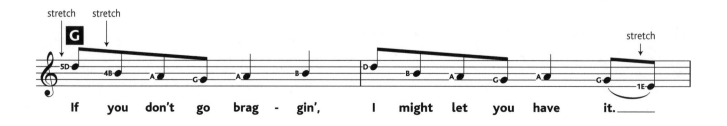

If you don't go brag - gin', I might let you have it.___

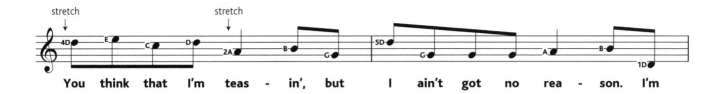

You think that I'm teas - in', but I ain't got no rea - son. I'm

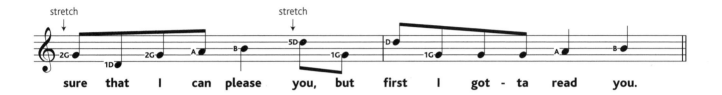

sure that I can please you, but first I got - ta read you.

Ooh, boy, you look - ing like you like what you see. Won't you

come ov - er and check up on it? I'm - a let you work up on it.

La - dies, let him check up on it watch it while he check up on it.

Dip it, pop it, twirk it, stop it; check on me to - night.

Crazy

Words & Music by Thomas Callaway, Brian Burton, Gianfranco Reverberi & Gian Piero Reverberi

Voice: **Piano**
Rhythm: **8th beat Pop**
Tempo: ♩ = 112

I re-mem-ber when, I re-mem-ber, I re-mem-ber when I lost my

mind. There was some-thing so plea-sant a-bout that place.

Ev-en your e-mo-tions had an e-cho in so much

space. And when you're out there, with-out

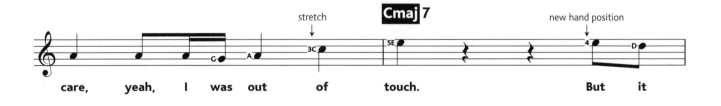

care, yeah, I was out of touch. But it

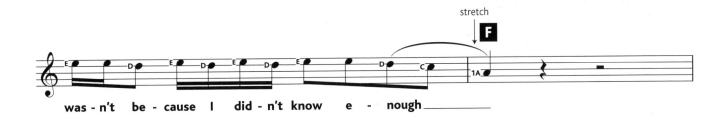

was - n't   be - cause   I   did - n't   know   e - nough

I   just   knew   too   much.   Does   that   make   me   cra -

- zy?   Does   that   make   me   cra   -   zy?

Does   that   make   me   cra   -   zy?   Pos - sib -

- ly.   Well,   I   think   you're   cra   -   zy,

I   think   you're   cra   -   zy.   I   think   you're   cra   -   zy.

Just   like   me.   May - be   we're   cra - zy.

13

Crystal Ball

Words & Music by Richard Hughes, James Sanger, Tim Rice-Oxley & Tom Chaplin

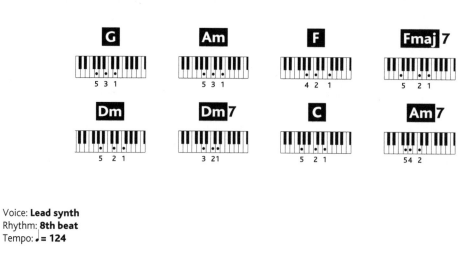

Voice: **Lead synth**
Rhythm: **8th beat**
Tempo: ♩ = 124

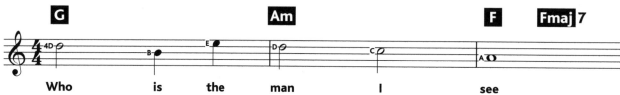

Who   is   the   man   I   see

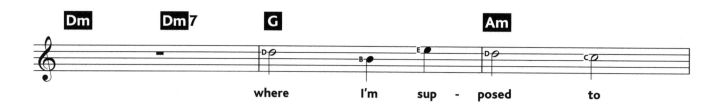

where   I'm   sup - posed   to

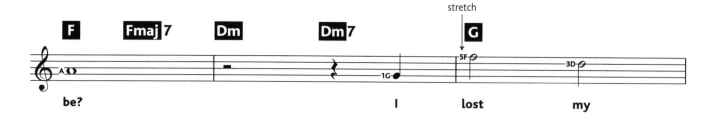

be?   I   lost   my

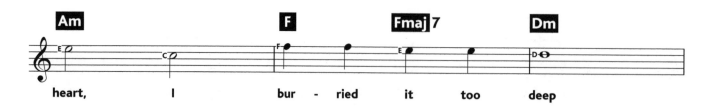

heart,   I   bur - ried   it   too   deep

un - der   the   ir - on   sea._____

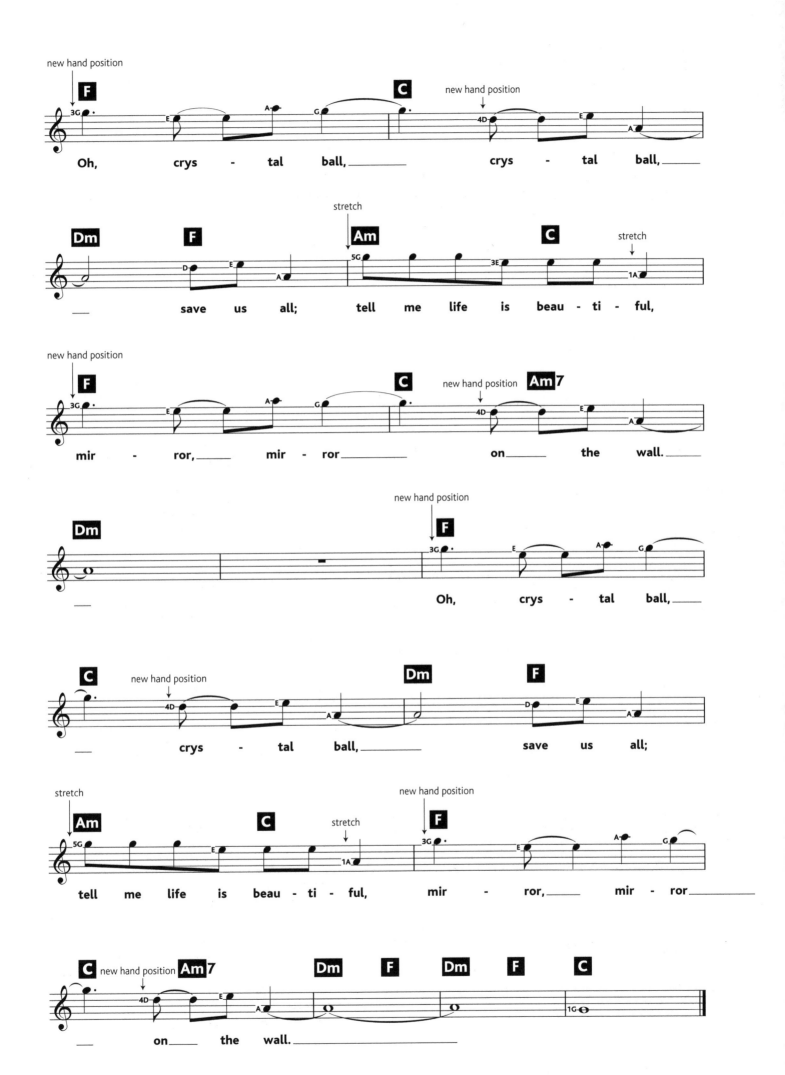

Fix You

Words & Music by Coldplay, Guy Berryman, Chris Martin, Jon Buckland & Will Champion

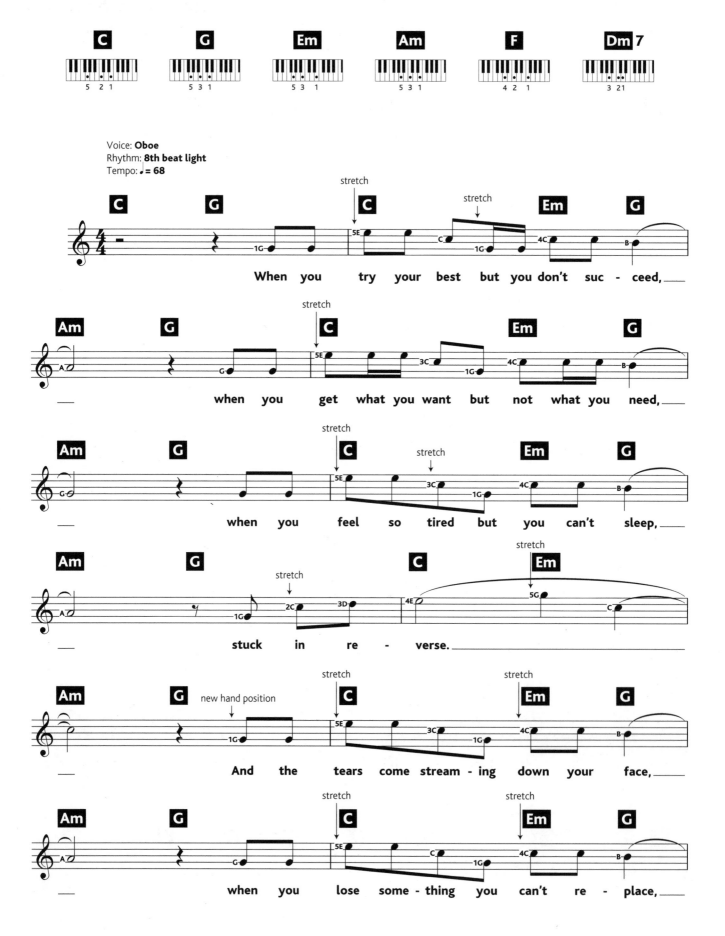

Voice: **Oboe**
Rhythm: **8th beat light**
Tempo: ♩ = 68

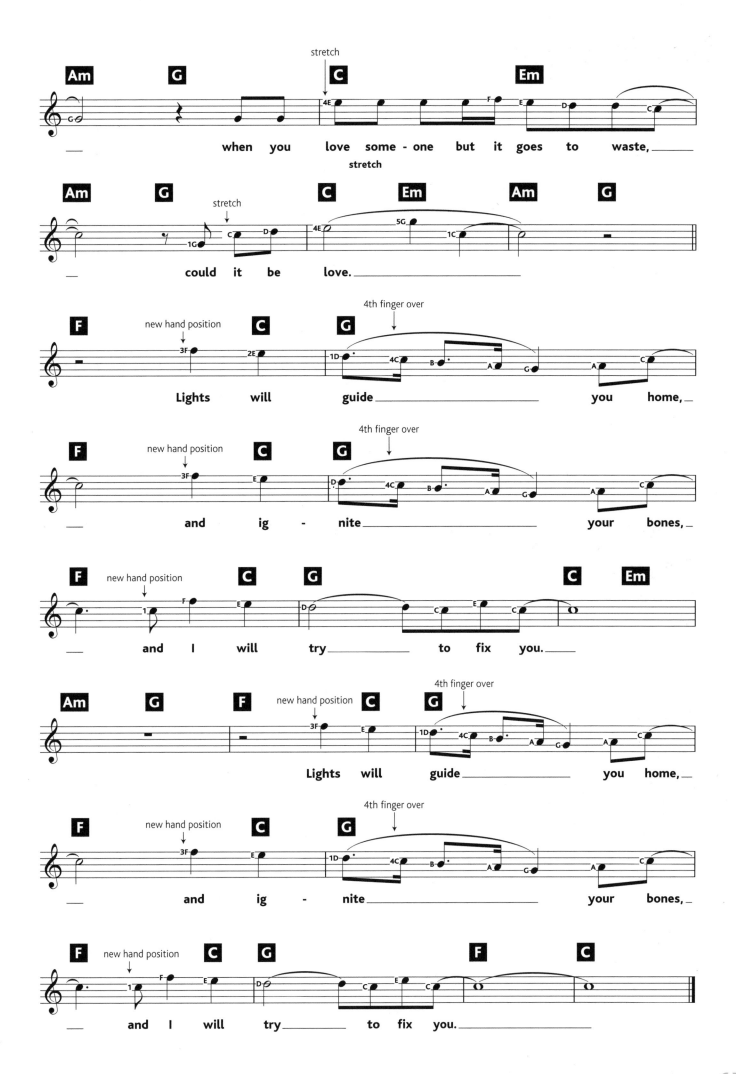

No Tomorrow

Words & Music by George Astasio, Christopher Cano, Jason Pebworth, Chad Rachild, Kevin Roentgen & John Bentjen

Voice: **Jazz organ**
Rhythm: **8th beat**
Tempo: ♩ = 124

Let's go to a rave and be - have like we're trip - pin' sim - ply

'cause we're so in love. Fun - ny

hats, shi - ny pants, all we need for some ro - mance. Go get

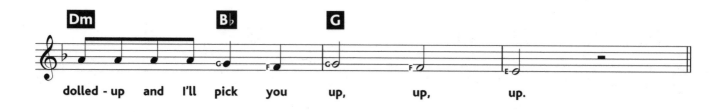

dolled - up and I'll pick you up, up, up.

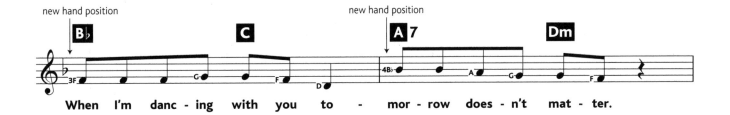

When I'm danc - ing with you to - mor - row does - n't mat - ter.

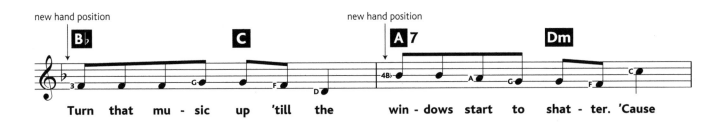

Turn that mu - sic up 'till the win - dows start to shat - ter. 'Cause

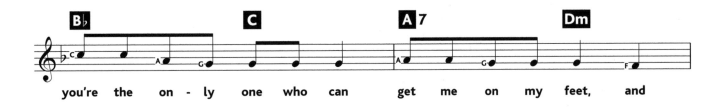

you're the on - ly one who can get me on my feet, and

I can't ev - en dance. _____

Ev - 'ry - bo - dy here is star - ing at the out - fit that you're wear - ing

love it when they check you____ out.

Cov - er's on - ly twen - ty bucks, and ev - en if the D. - J. sucks it's

time to turn this mu - tha _____ out!

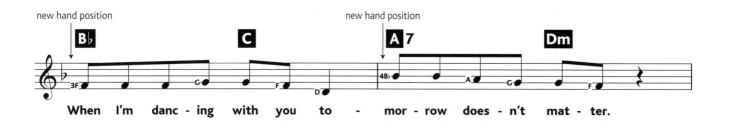

When I'm danc - ing with you to - mor - row does - n't mat - ter.

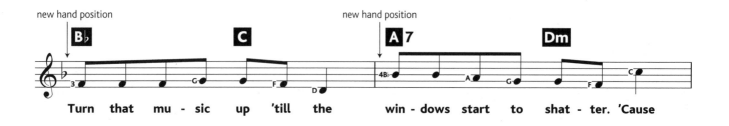

Turn that mu - sic up 'till the win - dows start to shat - ter. 'Cause

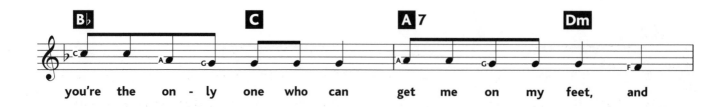

you're the on - ly one who can get me on my feet, and

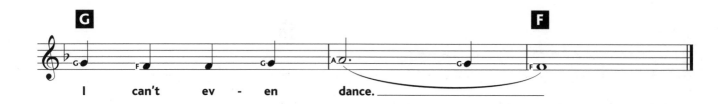

I can't ev - en dance. _____

That's My Goal

Words & Music by Jörgen Elofsson, Bill Padley & Jeremy Godfrey

Voice: **Flute**
Rhythm: **6/8**
Tempo: ♩ = 72

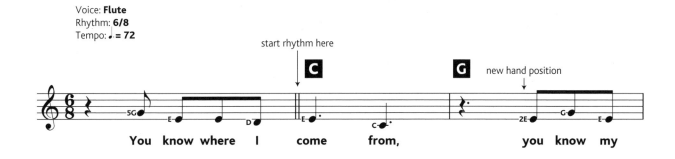

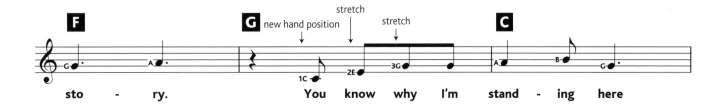

You know where I come from, you know my

sto - ry. You know why I'm stand - ing here

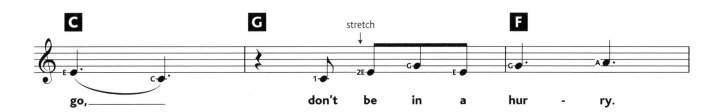

to - night. Please don't ____

go, ____ don't be in a hur - ry.

G new hand position   C   G

I'm here to make it clear, make it

right.   Well,   I   know   I've   act -   ed

fool -   ish   but   I   pro -   mise   you   no   more.   I've

fin -   ally   found   that   some -   thing   worth   reach -   ing

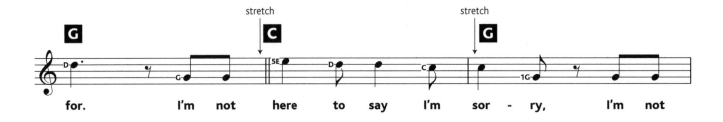

for.   I'm   not   here   to   say   I'm   sor -   ry,   I'm   not

here   to   lie   to   you.   I'm   here   to   say   I'm

rea -   dy,   that   I've   fin -   ally   thought   it   through.   I'm   not

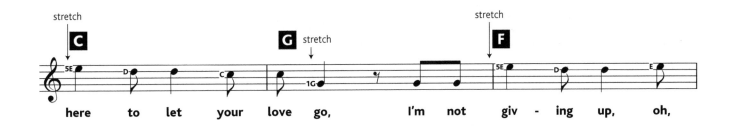

here   to   let   your   love   go,   I'm   not   giv -   ing   up,   oh,

no.   I'm   here   to   win   your   heart   and

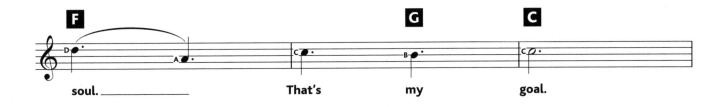

soul. _____   That's   my   goal.

I'm   not   here   to   let   your   love   go,   I'm   not

giv -   ing   up,   oh,   you.   I'm   here   to   win   your

heart   and   soul. _____   That's   my   goal.

Other Side Of The World

Words & Music by KT Tunstall & Martin Terefe

Voice: **Saxophone**
Rhythm: **8th beat**
Tempo: ♩ = 80

Ov - er the sea and far a - way she's wait-ing like an ice - berg, wait-ing to

change. But she's cold in - side, she wants to be like the wa - ter.___

All the mus - cles tight - en in her face, bu - ries her

soul in one em - brace.___ They're one and the same, just like wa - ter.___

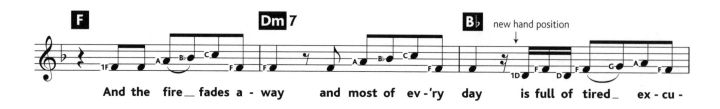

And the fire___ fades a - way and most of ev -'ry day is full of tired___ ex - cu -

- ses but it's too hard to say. I wish it were sim - ple but we give up ea - si -

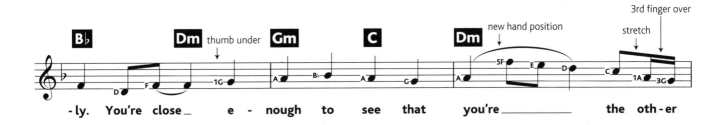

- ly. You're close e - nough to see that you're the oth - er

side of the world to me. And the fire fades a - way and most of ev - 'ry

day is full of tired ex - cu - ses but it's too hard to say. I wish it were sim -

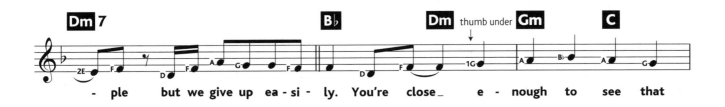

- ple but we give up ea - si - ly. You're close e - nough to see that

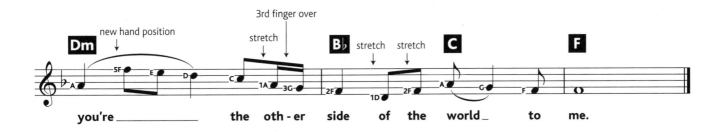

you're the oth - er side of the world to me.

Put Your Records On

Words & Music by John Beck, Steven Chrisanthou & Corinne Bailey Rae

She Moves In Her Own Way

Words & Music by Luke Pritchard, Hugh Harris, Max Rafferty & Paul Garred

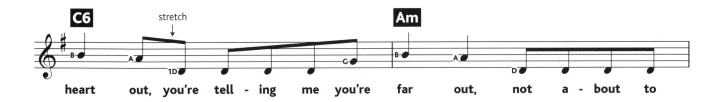

heart out, you're tell - ing me you're far out, not a - bout to

lie down for your cause. But you don't pull my strings, 'cause I'm a

bet - ter man, mov - ing on to bet - ter things. But uh

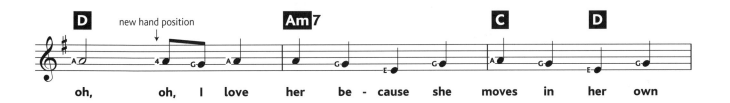

oh, oh, I love her be - cause she moves in her own

way. But uh oh, oh, she came to my show just to

hear a - bout my day. But uh oh, oh, I love

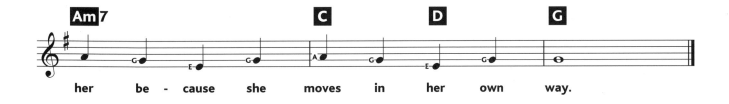

her be - cause she moves in her own way.

Unfaithful

Words & Music by Mikkel Eriksen, Tor Erik Hermansen & Shaffer Smith

Voice: **Piano**
Rhythm: **8th beat light**
Tempo: ♩ = 72

Stor - y of my life, search - ing for the right, but it keeps a - void - ing me.

Sor - row in my soul, 'cause it seems that wrong, real ly loves my com - pa - ny. And I know that

he knows I'm un - faith - ful and it kills him in - side, to know that I am

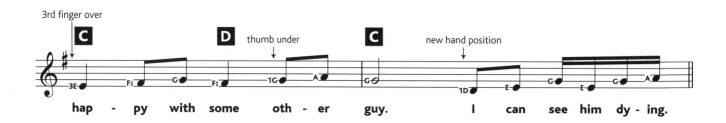

hap - py with some oth - er guy. I can see him dy - ing.

I don't want to do this an - y - more, ___ I don't want to be the rea - son

why, ev-'ry time I walk out the door,___ I see him die a lit-tle more in-

- side, I don't want to hurt him an-y-more, I don't want to take a-way his

life, I don't want to be, a murd-er-

- er. I can see him dy-ing.

I don't want to do this an-y-more,___ I don't want to be the rea-son

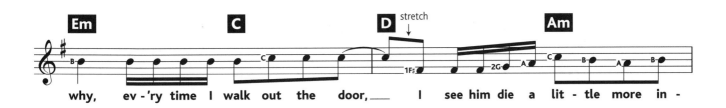

why, ev-'ry time I walk out the door,___ I see him die a lit-tle more in-

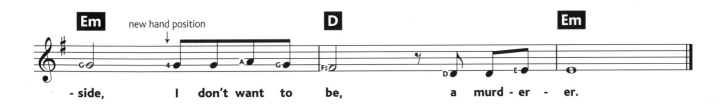

- side, I don't want to be, a murd-er-er.

Who Am I

Words & Music by Francis White & Lucie Silverman

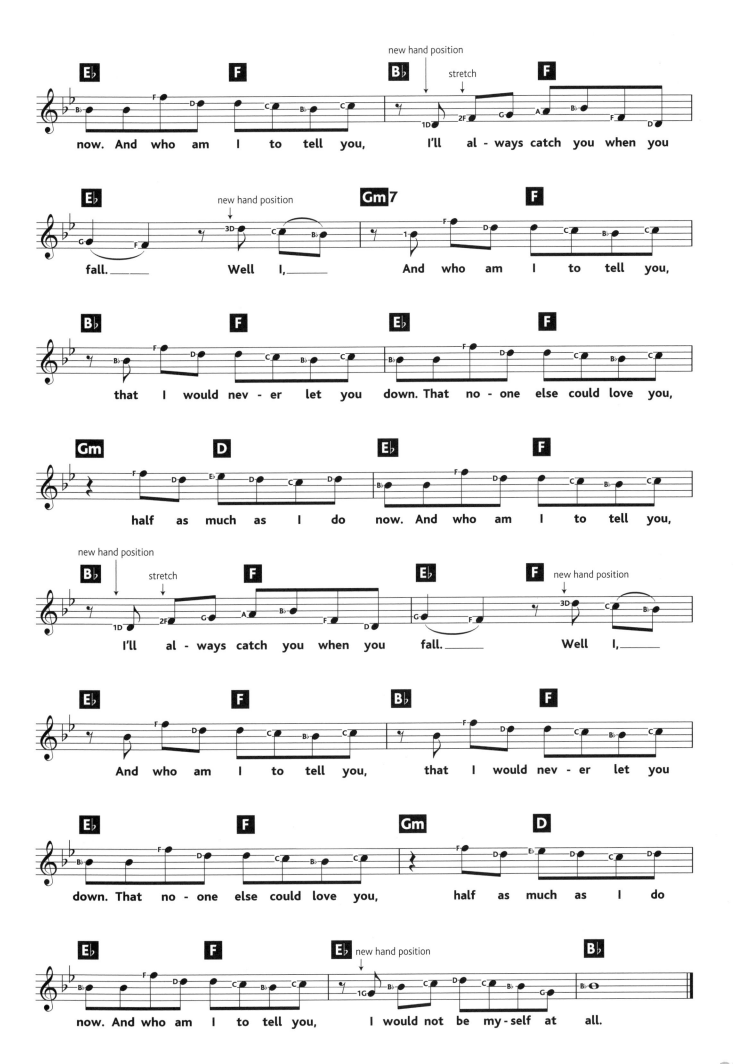

Wisemen

Words & Music by James Blunt, James Hogarth & Sacha Skarbek

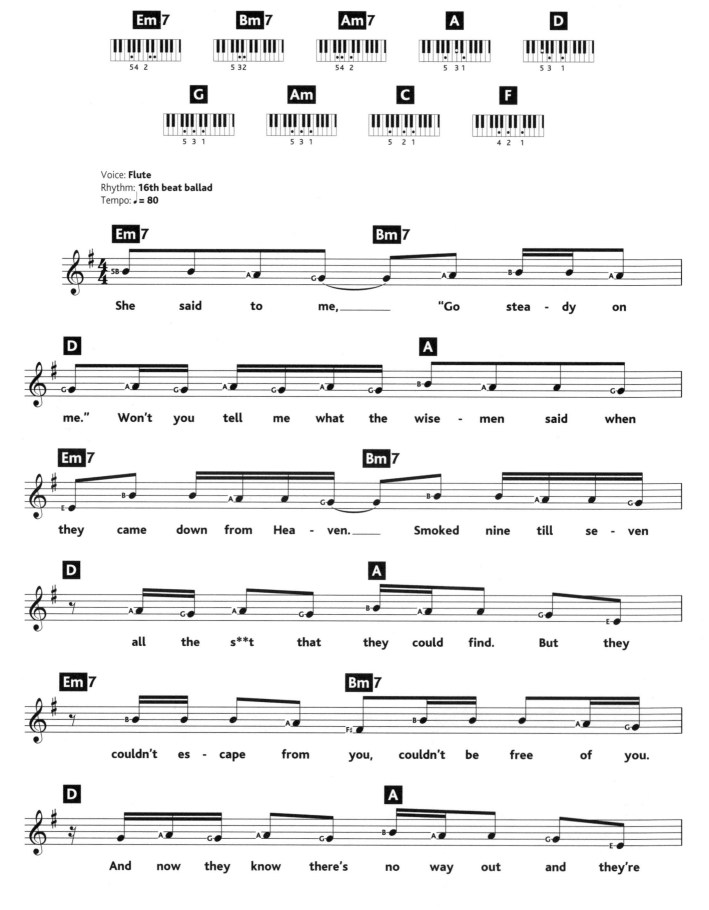

real - ly sor - ry now for what they've done. They were

three wise men just try - in' to have some fun.   Look who's a - lone now, it's not

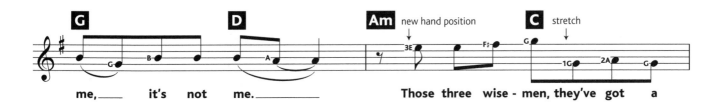

me,___ it's not me.___   Those three wise - men, they've got a

se - mi by the sea.___   Got - ta ask your - self the ques - tion,

where are you now?   Got - ta ask your - self the ques - tion

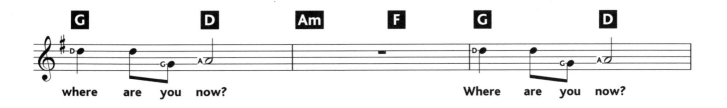

where are you now?   Where are you now?

Got - ta ask your - self the ques - tion where are you now?___

You Give Me Something

Words & Music by Francis White & James Morrison

-right. This could be___ noth-ing,___ but I'm will-ing to give__ it a try.__

___ Please give me___ some-thing, 'cause some-day I might

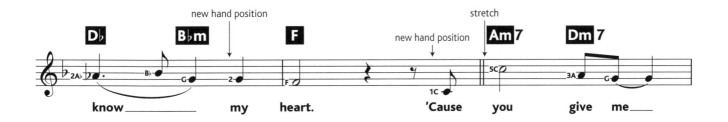

know_____ my heart. 'Cause you give me___

some-thing that makes me scared, al - right. This could be___

noth - ing,___ but I'm will-ing to give it a try.___ Please give me___

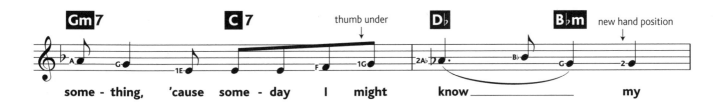

some-thing, 'cause some-day I might know_____ my

heart, I might know_____ my heart

Who Knew

Words & Music by Alecia Moore, Lukasz Gottwald & Max

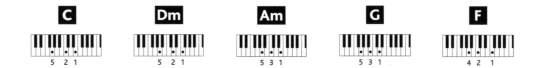

Voice: **Clarinet**
Rhythm: **8th beat**
Tempo: ♩ = 136

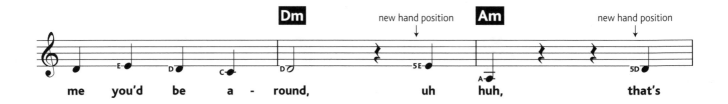

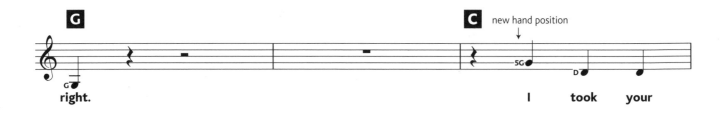

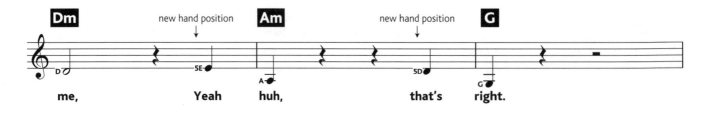

If some-one said three years from

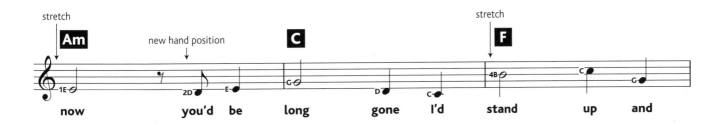

now you'd be long gone I'd stand up and

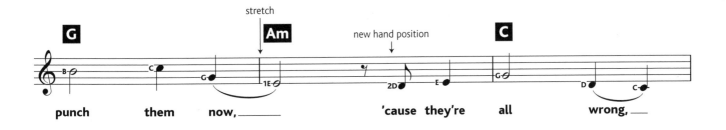

punch them now,_____ 'cause they're all wrong,_____

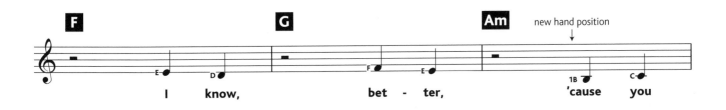

I know, bet - ter, 'cause you

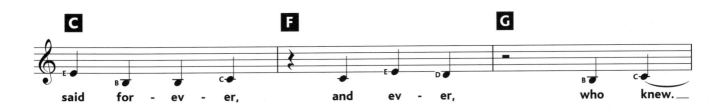

said for - ev - er, and ev - er, who knew._____

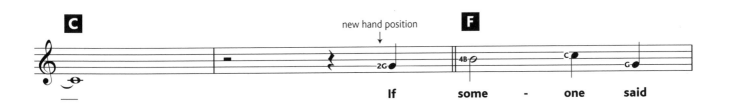

If some - one said

three   years   from   now   you'd be   long   gone   I'd

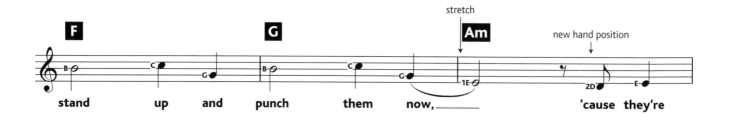

stand   up   and   punch   them   now, _____   'cause they're

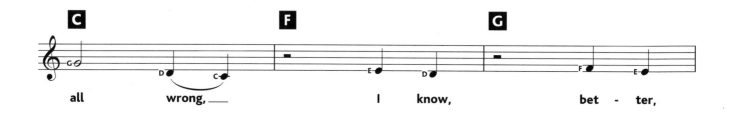

all   wrong, _____   I   know,   bet - ter,

'cause you   said   for - ev - er,   and   ev - er,

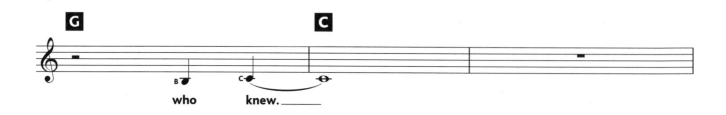

who   knew. _____

and ev - er,   who   knew. _____

1 2 3 4 5 6 7 8 9